Nita Mehta
PUBLICATIONS
Enriching Young Minds

ANURAG MEHTA

First Hardbound Edition 2009

ISBN 978-81-7676-096-6

*Illustrations:* Nita Mehta Publications — Enriching Young Minds

Artist: Artlab India

*Layout and laser typesetting:*

National Information Technology Academy
3A/3, Asaf Ali Road
New Delhi-110002

*Published by:*

**3A/3 Asaf Ali Road, New Delhi-110002**
***Tel:* 91-11-23250091, 29214011, 23252948, 29218574**
*Fax:*91-11-29225218, 91-11-23250091
*E-Mail* : nitamehta@email.com
nitamehta@nitamehta.com
*Website* : http://www.nitamehta.com
http://www.snabindia.com

*Contributing Writers:*
Subhash Mehta
Tanya Mehta

*Editorial & Proofreading:*
Ritika Sabbharwal

*Printed at:*
BATRA ART PRESS

*Distributed by:*
THE VARIETY BOOK DEPOT
A.V.G. Bhavan, M 3 Con Circus
New Delhi - 110 001
Tel: 23417175, 23412567; Fax: 23415335
E-mail: varietybookdepot@rediffmail.com

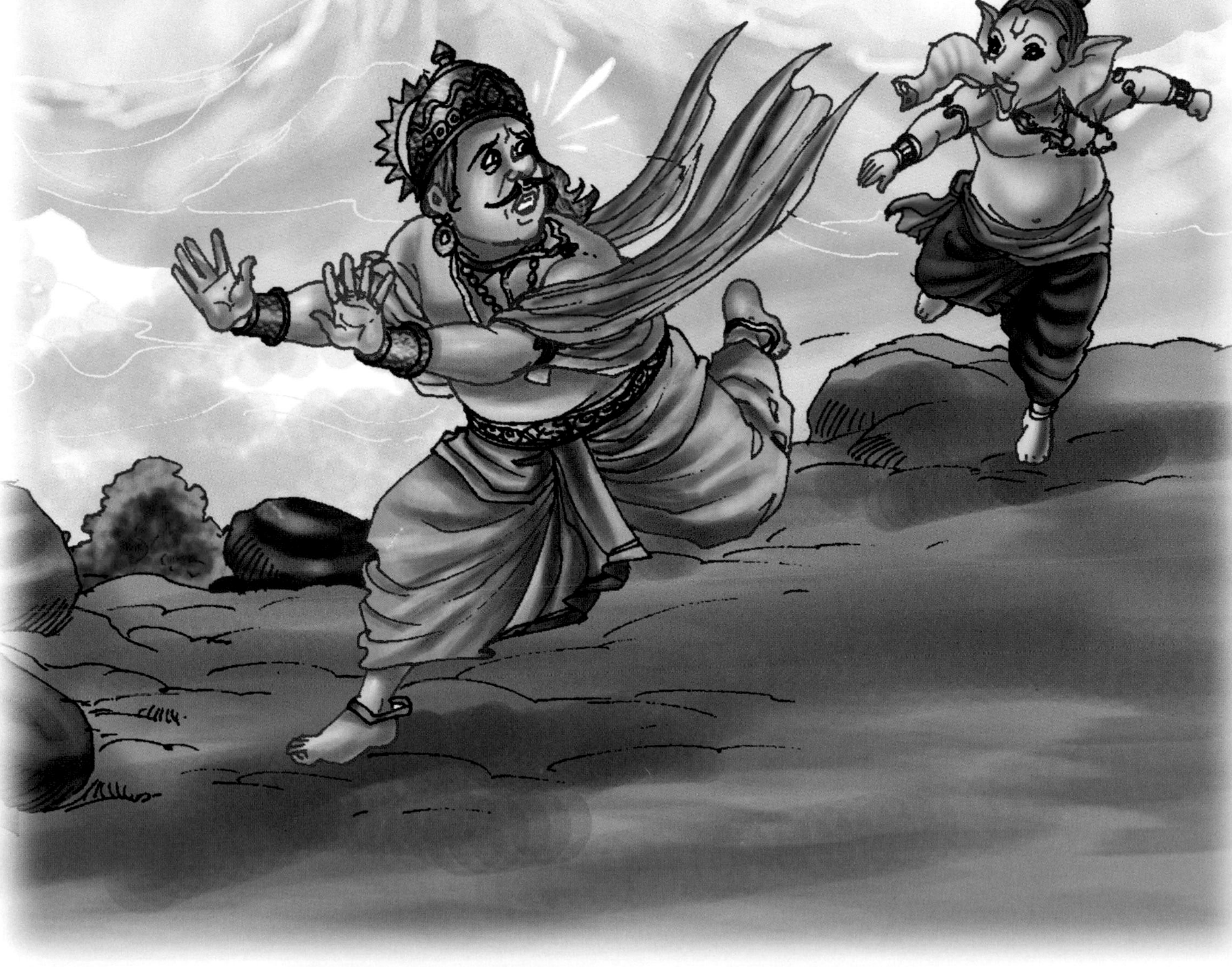

# Introduction

The Hindu religion has many Gods, although they are manifestations of the same divine form. Among the many deities worshipped by the Hindus, Lord Ganesha has a special place in the hearts of people. No worship of any kind or of any other deity can begin without an initial worship to Ganesha. For thousands of years in the villages of India, Lord Ganesha has been worshipped. Today, in towns and cities of many countries, Lord Ganesha has a powerful and immediate presence in everyone's lives. He was and is the one prayed to when starting a business or an enterprise of any kind. Even factory workers approach a small shrine dedicated to him before commencing their daily work, so that nothing goes wrong. Businessmen ask for Ganesha's help in adjusting the stock market to their advantage, and farmers, too, chant his 108 names while planting their seeds, rice, crops or trees. When grandma is sick or the crops don't arrive on time, Hindus diligently pray to this loving God for help in restructuring their lives through proper guidance and direction.

# CONTENTS

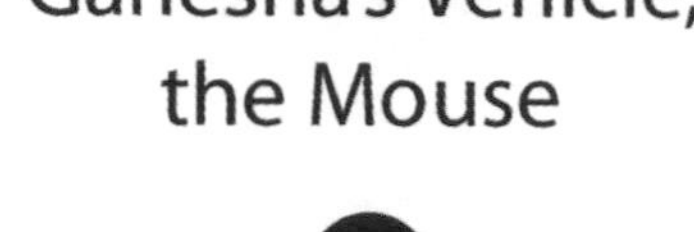

# Who is Ganesha?

Ganesha is the elephant headed Hindu God. He is the son of Lord Shiva and Goddess Parvati. Ganesha is the bearer of wisdom and good will. Revered by Hindus, there are 108 names of veneration for Lord Ganesha!

Ganesha even has his own vehicle to ride. Do you know what? A mouse!

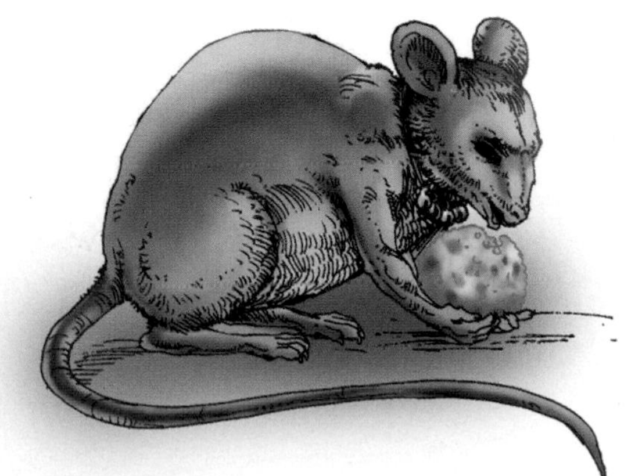

Thus, it is said that Ganesha has the extreme strength of an elephant to bulldoze his way on the surface and also the intricate agility of a mouse to burrow and manoeuvre under the surface!

Where does Ganesha live? He lives in the heavenly abode called *Kailash*. Does Ganesha have any brother or sister? Yes! He has a brother named Kartekeya.

Shiva and Parvati, like any other parents, had their hands full in bringing up Ganesha. Ganesha was an adorable cherub with all the naughtiness of a young boy. However, sometimes his profound wisdom surprised every one, including his parents.

# How Ganesha Got his Elephant Head?

The myth of Ganesha's elephant head has its origin in the story of his birth.

## Ganesha's Encounter with Shiva:

The most popular legend says that one day Goddess Parvati had to go for a bath but did not have anyone to guard her home.

"I need to go for a bath! But I am alone and there is no one to guard my home," fretted Goddess Parvati to herself. Why was the Goddess alone? Well, her husband Lord Shiva was away fighting wars with the demons. Parvati thought for some time and then decided, "I will create my own guard."

She rubbed her body with jasmine oil and sandal paste. Then, scraping off some of the scented paste from her body, she mixed it with water and clay from the river *Ganga* and made a clay boy from it. Holding the clay child close to her lips, Parvati infused life into him. And lo behold! The clay child became a handsome young boy. "You are our son from now on," Parvati proudly told the boy. "Guard my home whilst I bathe! Do not allow anyone to intrude or enter the hut," she instructed the boy. Then she went in for a bath. The boy stood in strict vigil. Unexpectedly, Lord Shiva returned home.

"Who are you?" Shiva questioned the boy who was not allowing him to enter his own home. "Who are you?" countered the boy!

Now, Lord Shiva, master of the universe and manifestation of the supreme almighty, was not at all pleased! He bristled and frowned demanding to be allowed to enter his home. However, the boy persistently refused to let Shiva enter. Shiva became very angry and a clash ensued. The fall out was that Shiva chopped the boy's head off. When Parvati came out of her bath, she was horrified to see what had happened.

Cursing Shiva, she wept uncontrollably. Shiva too was stricken with shock and grief. Unwittingly, he had killed his own son! He had to do something to comfort his grieving spouse. So, he turned to the other Gods and his attendants and said, "Go into the forest and bring the head of the first living being you see sleeping, facing the north."

"Why north?" wondered the Gods and Shiva's attendants.

"The northward journey means a journey towards illumination to the path of Gods. Moreover, we all know that the direction north is a beneficial one," explained Lord Shiva.

The attendants immediately followed his command. Soon, they came across an elephant who was sleeping, facing the north. The attendants cut its head off and gave it to Shiva. Shiva immediately placed the head on the lifeless boy's severed neck. With his new elephant head, the boy came alive. "We will name our son Ganesha meaning the God with the elephant head," proclaimed Shiva.

"I declare that Ganesha shall be regarded by one and all, as the remover of obstacles and he should be worshipped first, before any form of worship is offered to any other Gods," Shiva announced. Ganesha was also made the leader of Shiva's *ganas* (assistants) and thus became *Ganapati*. Parvati was overjoyed. It did not matter to her that her son now had an elephant head. He was well and alive and that's all she wanted.

## The Eye of Destruction:

Another legend has it that Parvati longed for a child and conveyed her desire to Shiva. He asked her to undertake the *Punyaka* penance for one year. During this period, the sage, Sanatkumara, presided over the austerities and made Parvati undergo several trials and tribulations to test her strength.

Finally, after she had passed all the tests and completed the vow undertaken by her, she heard a voice from the heavens telling her to look for her newborn son in her chamber.

When she ran in and saw the beautiful boy, she could not believe her eyes. He was more beautiful than all the Gods combined, and his face shone like the morning sun. Her joy knew no bounds.

All the Gods and Goddesses rushed to Mount Kailash, the abode of the divine parents, to see this child of glory. They paid obeisance and marvelled at the beauty of the child.

The nine *grahas* or planets also came to greet the divine couple and their beloved son. One of them, Shani (Saturn), would not however look up at the child and had his head bent. When Parvati asked him why he was reluctant to look at her son, he told her that there was a curse laid on him by his jealous wife, by which anyone he looked at with admiration would be destroyed.

Parvati, anxious like a fond mother for her son to be admired, insisted that he look at her son.

Shani then looked up at the child whose head immediately got separated from the body and flew off into space. Parvati wailed and lamented so loudly and created such commotion that the Gods rushed to Kailash.

Seeing what had happened, Vishnu, got on to his vehicle, *Garuda*, the eagle and flew in search of a head to replace the lost one.

On the banks of the River Pushpabhadra, he found a herd of elephants sleeping. Choosing an animal lying with its head to the north, he brought the head of an elephant (who was actually a *Gandharva*, a celestial being, waiting to be released from earthly life), and placed it on the headless child's neck. Breathing life into the child, he presented it to Parvati who felt overjoyed having a son with the wisdom and power of an elephant.

Vishnu adorned the child with exquisite ornaments, as did Himavan, Parvati's father. Vishnu collected all heavenly beings together and led the worship of the child, giving him the eight names by which he came to be commonly known - Ganesha, Vighneshwara, Heramba, Gajaanana, Lambodara, Ekadanta, Soorpakarna and Vinayaka.

# Shiva Worships Ganapati

It is believed that no act whether of peace or war or daily living will succeed unless Ganesha is worshipped first.

This holds true not only for humans but also for heavenly beings. Shiva had declared that Ganapati should be invoked in prayer by one and all to ensure success. No act or prayer to any deity would succeed unless preceded by worship of Ganesha.

When Shiva set out to destroy the evil demon, Tripuraasura, he forgot his own ruling and rushed forth in great haste. However, as he got into his chariot, the nail in the wheel broke and the chariot was not stranded.

Amazed that such an event should have happened to him, Shiva stopped and pondered. He then realised that he had forgotten to pray to Ganesha and hence this obstacle. He then invoked the name of his son and set out, achieving success in the Tripuraantaka war.

This story emphasises the importance of prayer to Ganesha at the beginning of every activity.

# Ganesha's Vehicle, the Mouse

According to a legend, Ganesha broke his tusk himself during a war against Gajamukhaasura.

Gajamukha, a demon, did severe penance on the advice of Shukrachaarya, the guru of the *asuras* or demons, and obtained invincible powers from Shiva. He used these powers to harass the Gods who then rushed to Ganesha for help. Ganesha battled with the demon but realised that, thanks to the powers given by Shiva, the evil Gajamukhaasura could not be killed.

Ganesha then broke his right tusk and struck Gajamukha with it, cursing him to change into a mouse. Ganesha then got on to the back of the mouse and made it his vehicle, thereby keeping it under his control.

According to another *Puranic* story, Ganesha's mouse was really the *Gandharva*, Krauncha. Once, in the court of Indra, the king of the *Devas*, Krauncha insulted the sage, Vaamadeva. He was then cursed by the sage which turned him into a large mouse.

The mouse, true to its nature, entered the ashram of Sage Paraashara and caused great havoc to his dwelling as only a mouse can. The Rishi then prayed to *Vinayaka* or Ganesha to save his simple dwelling. Ganesha appeared, made the mouse his vehicle, and brought him under control.

The purpose of making the mouse Ganesha's vehicle was to keep the rodent, who tended to create havoc, under the control of *Ganapati*.

# The Race

One day, voices resounded in and out of the environs of Mount Kailash. The two brothers, Ganesha and Kartekeya were arguing.

“Brother, believe me! I am older than you,” Ganesha stated as a matter of fact.

“No!” contradicted his brother Kartekeya, “I am the elder between the two.”

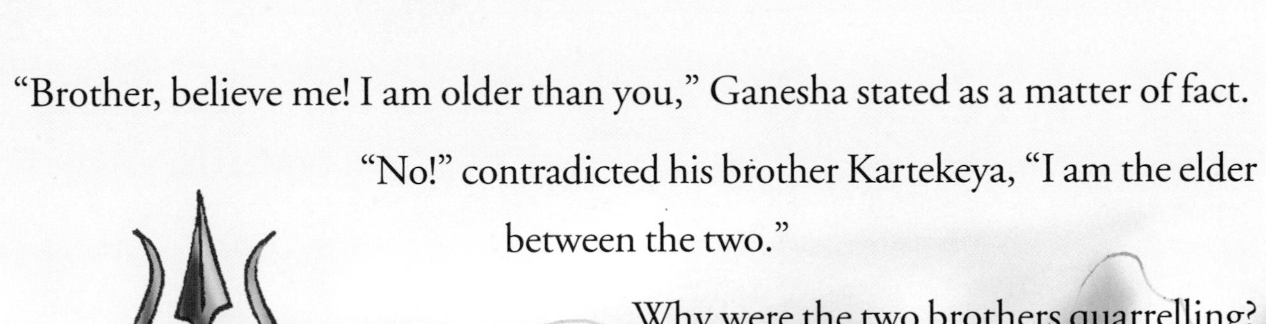

Why were the two brothers quarrelling? Actually, it all started when the Gods of heaven presented Shiva and Parvati with a rare fruit. Now the brothers verbally tangled over who should get the fruit.

“The elder one should,” mused their parents. Sigh! And that’s how a strife between the brothers ensued. Soon, the dispute heated up and finally their parents had to intervene. “Father, tell him that I am the elder of the two! I should get the fruit,” blurted Ganesha, his trunk curling and whirling in agitation.

Kartekeya shrugged saying, “Father, mother! Convince Ganesha that I am elder!”

“This is getting quite serious,” Shiva whispered to his wife.

“Yes! The brothers are getting into a terrible quarrel. Do something,” Parvati urged.

“Very well,” Shiva pondered and then spoke,

“Sons, we will resolve your argument with a solution. Whoever can tour the whole world and come back first to this starting point, will be given the right to be the elder brother and get the fruit.”

"Here I go," declared Kartekeya. Before anything, he flew off at once on his vehicle, the peacock, to make a trip around the world.

But Ganesha did not move. His vehicle, the mouse, was raring to go, but Ganesha just sat on it.

Did Ganesha move eventually? Did he begin the race? Well, yes he did. He moved, not to dash around the world, but only to circle his parents, who were very surprised.

Why was Ganesha still here? How would he cross continents, mountains, rivers and lakes if he did not leave?

Ganesha just kept circling his parents without a care in the world. His parents stared at him, confoundedly.

In a while, Ganesha came up to his parents and said,

"Divine parents, I have circled the world so many times. Give me the fruit and declare me first."

"Ganesha, we cannot do that. You did not circle the world with its seas, mountains and continents. You just hovered and circled around us," admonished his parents gently.

"But I have circled the world and come first father," Ganesha insisted.

"How?" questioned the two puzzled parents.

Ganesha bowed in front of Shiva and Parvati and said solemnly, "You two, are the world! My heavenly parents represent the entire manifested universe."

Hearing this, Shiva and Parvati broke into a cheer and proudly acknowledged that for a boy so young, Ganesha was really very wise. When Kartekeya returned, he was told of what Ganesha had said. He too agreed that Ganesha had shown very mature wisdom. Thus, Ganesha was declared the elder of the two and given the precious fruit.

Ganapati and
the God of Wealth

"I really have a lot of riches," bragged Kuber, the treasurer of the heavens, vainly to himself.

"I think I will go to Mount Kailash and invite Lord Shiva and his wife Goddess Parvati for a meal. They will come to my celestial kingdom of Alkapuri and see for themselves how wealthy I am."

Deciding this, Kuber went to Lord Shiva.

"Thank you so much Kuber, for your kind invitation," answered Shiva to Kuber's request for lunch.

"But, I am afraid, I will have to refuse," continued Shiva, "Parvati and I have pressing engagements elsewhere."

Shiva knew quite well why he was being invited. Kuber had always been a silly show-off. Kuber was unable to hide his disappointment, so Shiva quickly added, "I suggest you take Ganesha with you for lunch."

Ganesha nodded his head happily. He loved food and a lunch invitation promised a great deal of good eats.

Kuber, of course, kept boasting about his glory and his own riches as Ganesha accompanied him back to Alkapuri.

As soon as they reached Alkapuri, Ganesha was greeted with a traditional perfumed bath as part of an extravagant welcome at the palace entrance. After that, they entered into the luxurious palace. Kuber proudly strutted along the ornate corridors, hoping Ganesha was noticing his prosperity.

Ganesha was then led to an exquisite dining area. Servants carrying trays, laden with food, lined the hall. Overjoyed, Ganesha sat down to eat. His appetite was ravenous. He finished off all that was served to him.

"Bring me more food. Get me all the cooked food in the kitchen," demanded Ganesha. Hurriedly, the palace servants ran up and down serving Ganesha who seemed to be famished. The servants huffed, puffed and panted, piling food into Ganesha's plate. Ganesha ate and ate and ate. Dishes emptied faster than they could be filled.

"I am still hungry," Ganesha said impatiently, "I want more food."

"The food is finished, sire," the head cook whispered to Kuber.

Ganesha heard that and bellowed, "What? The food has finished!

But I am still hungry," Ganesha grabbed his plate and munched it up. The servants as well as Kuber shrank in fear. Ganesha ran to the kitchen and began to eat the empty vessels too! Then, he went to Kuber's treasury and began eating the pearls, gold and gems. Kuber saw his boundless treasure dwindling before his eyes, until all that remained were a couple of pearls in the corner. Kuber could have cried in anguish. His treasury had never looked so empty. Still, Ganesha was not satisfied.

Ganesha went on eating everything that came his way, even the furniture of the palace, the gardens, the trees, everything! He began to eat through the city of Alkapuri.

Kuber watched horrified. He stood with folded hands and appealed to Ganesha not to destroy his city.

"I am still hungry," said Ganesha. Then, Kuber noticed the little God looking at him with a wicked gleam in his eyes.

"Since there is nothing left to eat," said Ganesha, "I think I'll eat you."

Kuber fled with the little God close behind. He ran to Shiva and fell at his feet, quivering with fear.

"Help! My Almighty Lord, help! Ganesha is eating everything. His hunger is insatiable. He is threatening to eat me too. Save me," begged Kuber.

Shiva smiled and said,

"Kuber, take this roasted rice and feed Ganesha."

Kuber bowed humbly and served Ganesha. Ganesha ate the roasted rice and suddenly he was not hungry any more.

"I am full now," sighed Ganesha.

Kuber heaved a sigh of relief. He saw Ganesha and Shiva smiling at each other and realized he had been guilty of pride and vanity.

"Forgive me, Lord, for my false pride in my wealth. I had forgotten that it is you who gave it to me."

Thus, saying so, Kuber left.

Later, Kuber thought to himself,

"Lord Ganesha taught me a good lesson. By demanding more food, he was showing me that even the best of cuisine brought to him with an intention to show off, brings no satisfaction. Yet, just a handful of ordinary roasted rice, given with love and devotion gave him so much of contentment and he was happy. I was wrong to have expressed my love and devotion to God by material wealth and not by genuine feelings."

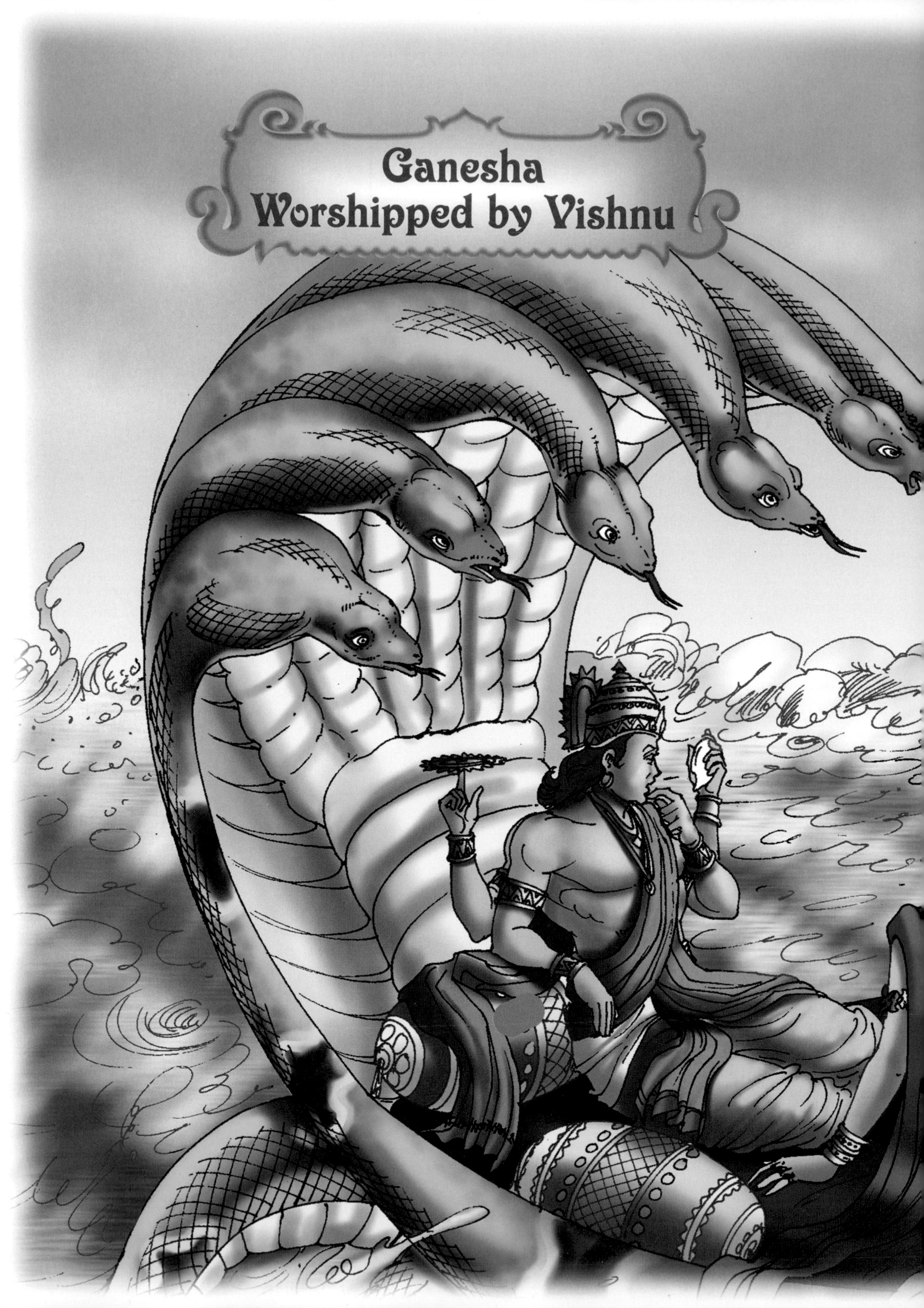
Ganesha
Worshipped by Vishnu

Another similar story concerns Vishnu. As a child, Ganesha used to play with Shiva's *ganas* at the foot of Mount Kailash, the abode of Shiva and Parvati. Hiding in a flower garden, he would suck in water from the Ocean of Milk (on which Vishnu lay on his serpent *Ananta*) and spray it on the *ganas,* teasing them that it was raining.

Vishnu, one day, found that his *Valamburi Shankh* (his sacred conch with swirls towards the right) was missing, and was perturbed. He then heard the deep resonant sound of a conch and knew that it was his sacred Shankh being blown in the vicinity of Mount Kailash.

He now looked towards Shiva who said that anyone wishing to retrieve the conch should pray to Valamburi Ganesha (Ganesha in the rare posture of his trunk turned to the right). Vishnu did accordingly and Ganapati then returned the sacred Shankh to its rightful owner, Vishnu, who was overjoyed to have it back.

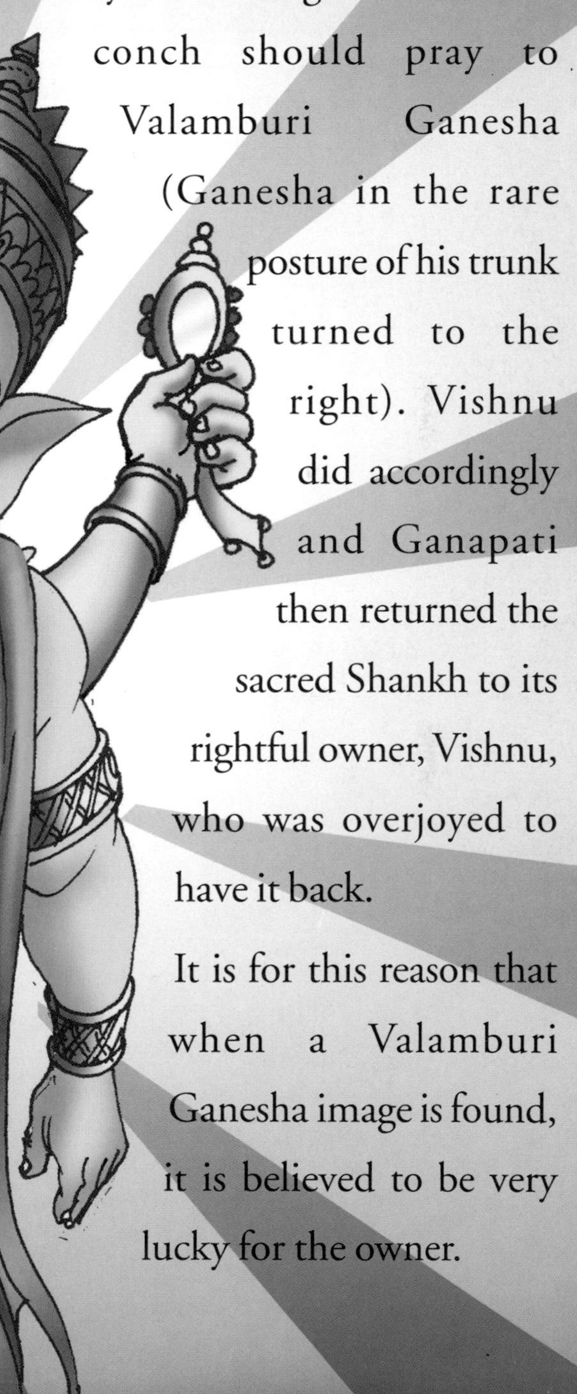

It is for this reason that when a Valamburi Ganesha image is found, it is believed to be very lucky for the owner.

# The Moon Teases Ganesha

"Aha, today is my birthday and I shall eat lots of *laddoos*," Ganesha slurped to his mouse.

"Let's go! A devotee has invited me to his house for a feast."

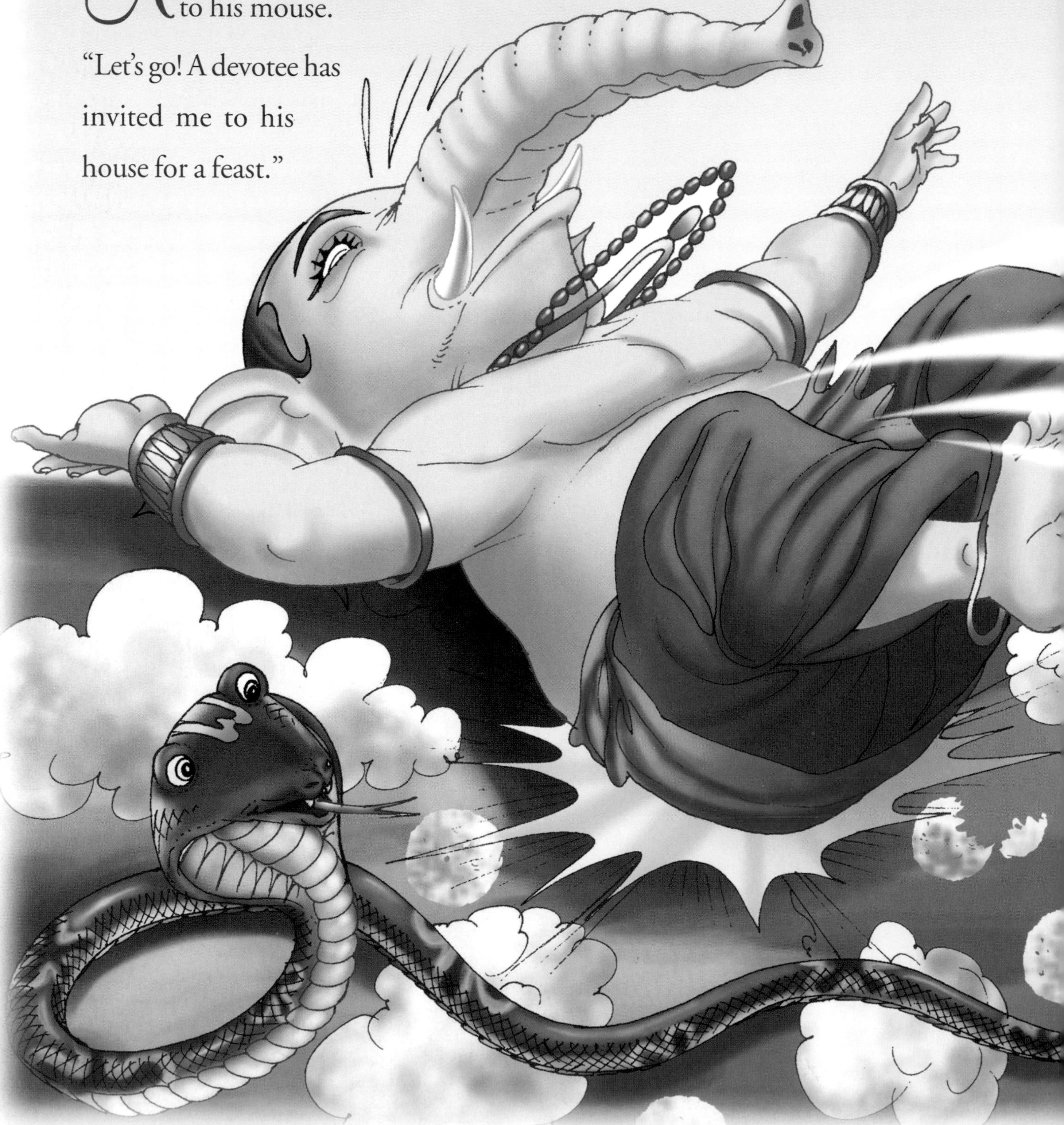

Ganesha was extremely happy when he saw the pile of *laddoos* set before him at the devotee's home.

"Munch-yum-munch-munch!" Ganesha eagerly picked off the *laddoos* with his trunk from the plate. He ate and ate till his belly began to swell. "Burp!" went Ganesha and his belly shook.

"Now, I am satisfied! I have eaten so many *laddoos* that I can hardly move. Mouse, take me home." He mounted his mouse and left.

The mouse with Ganesha on his back weaved through paths. Suddenly, a snake abruptly came in their way. The mouse skidded and in doing so, he threw Ganesha off!

Bump! Ganesha rolled and with a thump and his stomach burst open. Plonk-plonk-plonk! *Laddoos* spilled from his tummy. Horrified, Ganesha looked around, his trunk curling with acute embarrassment. He was sure that no one was around to see his ridiculous situation.

"Wait, mouse! Let me put the *laddoos* back into my stomach," Ganesha uttered. He quickly filled his stomach again, but realized that the *laddoos* kept spilling out from his open belly.

"Aha! I have an idea," Ganesha muttered, glancing at the slinking snake.

Whup! He seized the snake.

"Sorry snake, I am going to use you as a belt to hold my tummy full of *laddoos*."

Saying so, Ganesha did just that. He tightened the 'snake belt' and held back all the *laddoos* into his big belly.

"Let's go," Ganesha instructed his ride. Just as Ganesha remounted his vehicle, he heard a chuckle.

"Who is that?" Ganesha curiously flapped his ears and looked around. There was no one on the surface.

"Ha-ha-ha, so funny, ha-ha! Using a snake belt to stop *laddoos* from spilling," again someone giggled.

Now, Ganesha was extremely angry. Who was mocking him? He looked up and saw the culprit. It was the moon. The moon was giggling helplessly at the sight of Ganesha and his stomach full of *laddoos* tied with a snake.

Ganesha went crimson with anger.

"How dare you laugh at me?" shouted Ganesha at the moon. But the moon was quite taken in by the funny sight and kept smirking.

This further angered Ganesha and he broke a part of his tusk and hurled it at the moon, saying wrathfully, "I curse you! You will never shine at night now!"

Till then, the moon used to shine every night. But as soon as Ganesha cursed it, the moon disappeared and the sky went inky black. Ganesha rode off fuming.

"Aieeee!!! Where is the moon?" the people on earth frantically asked. "Where is the moon?" inquired the Gods in heaven too.

Nights became miserable for the residents on earth and heaven. Gloomy darkness besieged them every evening.

"This is Ganesha's doing. He is angry with the moon for laughing at him. Let's go and beg Ganesha to forgive the moon," suggested someone.

So people, accompanied by the Gods, went to Ganesha and pleaded, "Please bring the moon back. Please forgive it for laughing at you." Ganesha was not someone who carried grudges.

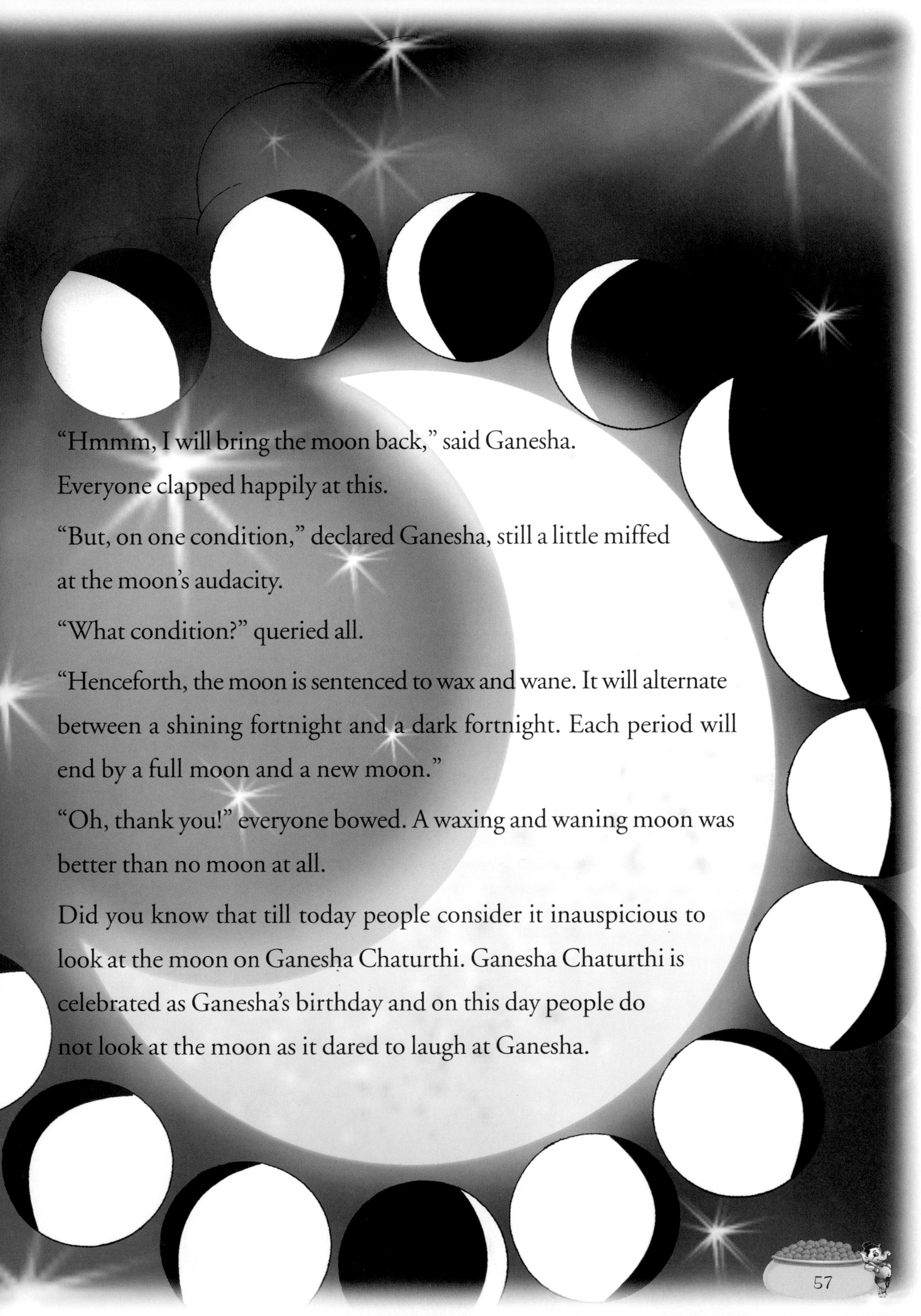

"Hmmm, I will bring the moon back," said Ganesha.

Everyone clapped happily at this.

"But, on one condition," declared Ganesha, still a little miffed at the moon's audacity.

"What condition?" queried all.

"Henceforth, the moon is sentenced to wax and wane. It will alternate between a shining fortnight and a dark fortnight. Each period will end by a full moon and a new moon."

"Oh, thank you!" everyone bowed. A waxing and waning moon was better than no moon at all.

Did you know that till today people consider it inauspicious to look at the moon on Ganesha Chaturthi. Ganesha Chaturthi is celebrated as Ganesha's birthday and on this day people do not look at the moon as it dared to laugh at Ganesha.

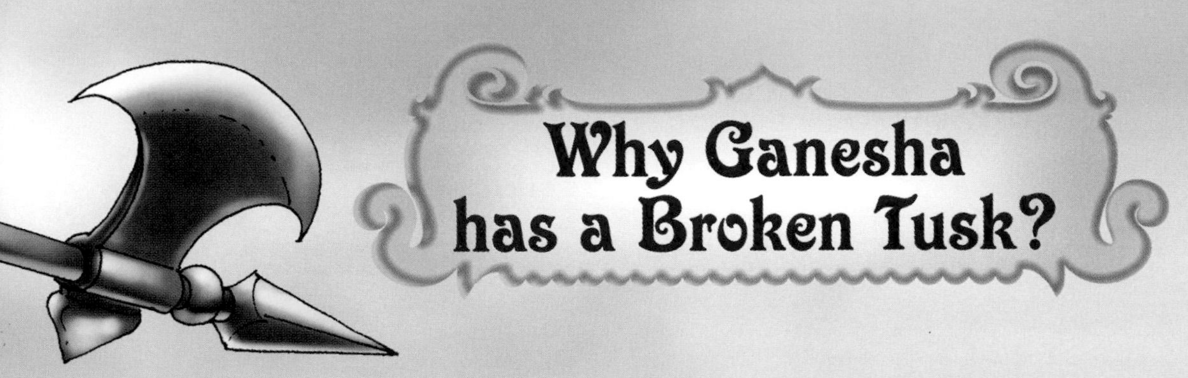

# Why Ganesha has a Broken Tusk?

There are several legends as to how Ganesha broke one of his tusks, giving him the name, *Ekadanta*, meaning the one with a single tusk.

One of them pertains to his battle with Parashurama.

*Parashurama* was one of the incarnations of Vishnu, born on earth to teach a lesson to the ruling classes, the *Kshatriyas*, who had become very arrogant and were riding roughshod over the ordinary people. As a human on earth, he meditated to Shiva and obtained the divine axe, *Parashu*, with whose help he waged wars against all the erring princes and cleared the world of their evil.

Deeply indebted to Shiva, he then came to Mount Kailash to pay obeisance to his mentor. Ganesha, who was guarding the entrance to his father's chambers, would not let him in, saying he had to wait till he obtained Shiva's permission. Parashurama felt that he, a devotee, needed no permission.

When Ganesha refused to give in, a hot tempered Parashurama, struck Ganesha's tusk with his axe. Ganesha recognized his father's axe and received it with respect. The blow of the axe broke Ganesha's tusk.

Shiva and Parvati appeared before him and chastised Parashurama. Realizing his mistake, Parashurama worshipped Ganesha and obtained his forgiveness and blessings.

# Ganesha and the Cat

As a child, Ganesha teased a cat by pulling its tail, rolling it over on the ground and causing it great pain as naughty young boys tend to do. After some time, he grew tired of his game and went to Kailash to his mother Parvati. He found her in great pain and covered with scratches and dust all over. When he questioned her, she blamed him for her pain and explained that she was the cat whom Ganesha had teased!

This story teaches us that all beings are part of divinity. Hurting one's fellow-creatures, human or animal, means hurting God himself just as Ganesha hurt Parvati by hurting the cat.

Ganesha learnt his lesson just as we all need to do so.

# Ganesha and the River Cauvery

To bring water to the arid areas of South India, Lord Shiva took the river Cauvery from his matted locks and filled it in *Agastyas' kamandalam* (spouted pot), bidding Cauvery to flow wherever *Agastya* pointed.

Agastya came down South wanting to find the ideal spot from which the river could flow, and reached the Kodagu (Coorg) hills.

River Cauvery was disrespectful to Agastya when he came down South. This angered the Sage and to teach her a lesson, Agastya imprisoned the entire river in his *kamandalam*, not letting it go.

The Gods felt anxious on seeing this and asked Lord Ganesha for help.

Ganesha disguised himself as a little boy and appeared before the Sage. The Sage had to go somewhere and asked the boy to hold the *kamandalam* while he was gone.

Ganesha, in his wisdom, selected the right place for the origin of the river, and left the *kamandalam* on the ground at the spot and left.

Later, Ganesha disguised himself as a crow and sat on the *kamandalam*. When Agastya returned and saw the crow, he shooed it away. When the crow flew off, it upset the *kamandalam* and set the river free; water gushing forth from the spot now known as *Talacauvery*.

With Ganesha's blessings, the benefits of the waters of the Cauvery are enjoyed to this day.

# Ganesha and Ravana

Ravana, the demon king of Lanka, was an ardent devotee of Lord Shiva. He reached Mount Kailash and undertook the most difficult *tapasyas* (austerities) which pleased Lord Shiva.

When Shiva appeared before Ravana to grant him a boon, Ravana asked that neither he nor his kingdom should ever be destroyed or harmed.

Shiva then gave him an *Atma Lingam*, the symbol of Shiva, and said that he should take it to his kingdom and set it up in a shrine with proper rituals. Only then would he become invincible. But there was one condition; Ravana should go back on foot to Lanka and on no account should the *Lingam* be placed on the ground as then it would remain firmly on that spot and become immovable.

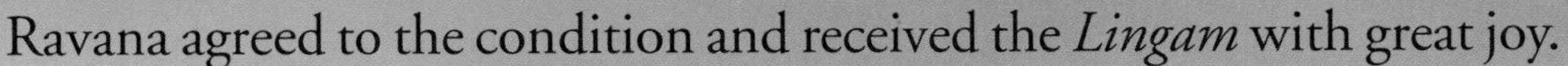

Ravana agreed to the condition and received the *Lingam* with great joy.

However, the Gods (*Devas*) were frightened with the consequences of Ravana obtaining all this power. The *Devas* were worried that the *Atma Lingam* would add to the might of Ravana and that he could never be destroyed if he succeeded in taking the *Atma Lingam* to Lanka. They prayed to Lord Ganesha for help.

Lord Ganesha caused Ravana's stomach to be filled with water. Ravana grew desperate to answer nature's call. Ganesha appeared before Ravana as a small boy. Ravana handed over the *Atma Lingam* to the boy to hold it.

Ganesha, disguised as the boy said,

"I cannot hold the *Lingam* for long and when I grow tired, I would call out your name thrice. If you do not return, then I would place it on the ground and go away."

Ravana agreed.

Soon Ganesha called out Ravana's name thrice, and since Ravana could not come and take the *Lingam*, he placed it on the ground. The enraged Ravana tried to remove the *Lingam* from the ground. But, in spite of using his twenty hands, he could not budge the Lingam. Though the Lingam could not be moved, the pressure from Ravana's hands had changed its shape like the ear of a cow and hence the place came to be called *Kokarnam* (*Ko* meaning cow, *karnam* meaning ear).

Ravana was furious and chased the boy, threatening to kill him.

The boy then revealed his true form as Ganesha. He overpowered Ravana, rolled him into a ball and threw him into the sky. Ganesha played with him as a child plays with a ball. Ravana realized how powerful Ganesha was and accepted his defeat.

# Ganesha and Duraasadan

Duraasadan, the son of the demon, Bhasmasura, did *tapasya* and pleased Lord Shiva. Shiva granted him the boon that all *Devas* would remain under his powers and Duraasadan would never die.

On fulfilment of this boon, there was total chaos. All the *Devas* ran into hiding and even Brahma and Vishnu ran out of their *Brahma Loka* and *Vaikuntha*.

All of them rushed to Kasi which was ruled by Viswanathar. On hearing this, Duraasadan came to Kasi. All the Gods and *Devas* rushed away to Kedaram.

Soon, on the prayers of the *Devas*, an *avaatar* of Lord Ganesha emerged from Goddess Parvati's face. This form of Ganesha had five faces and ten hands. Parvati named him *Vakradhundar* and gave him her vehicle, the lion.

There ensued a heavy fight between Vakradhundar and Duraasadan. Finally, Ganesha took a huge form (*Vishwaroopam*) and placed his feet on Duraasadan's head. As Ganesha touched him, all evil thoughts and the effects of his evil deeds rushed out of Duraasadan.

How did this happen? Ganesha being the form of knowledge and wisdom removed all evil from Duraasadan's mind. Then Lord Ganesha gave him the job of destroying all evil in Kasi. Hence the evil destroyer became the protector.

# Ganesha Writes the Mahabharata

Sage Ved Vyasa conceived a beautiful poem in his mind. He called it the *Mahabharata*. Ved Vyasa wanted to tell the whole world about his poem, but he did not know how to do so. He decided to meditate and ask the creator of the world, Lord Brahma, to suggest a way.

"Write the verses of this eloquent poem. Make a chronicle for future generations to read," Lord Brahma instructed sage Ved Vyasa.

"As you command, my Lord," Ved Vyasa bowed. He, however, added with folded hands, "Lord Brahma, I would like to request you to assign me an assistant."

"Ask Ganesha, the son of Shiva and Parvati," suggested Brahma.

"Will you be my assistant whilst I write the epic of Mahabharata?" the Sage asked Ganesha.

"Of course!" Ganesha nodded readily. "What do I have to do?"

"Well, I shall dictate verses and you shall write them down," answered the sage.

"No problem!" Ganesha said.

"But there are conditions, Ganesha," Ved Vyasa warned.

"What conditions, sire?" Ganesha asked.

"I will narrate the story and you must take it down as fast as I say it. Do not interrupt or ask me to repeat," instructed Ved Vyasa.

Lord Ganesha agreed but he had conditions too. Ganesha said to the sage, "I will do so. But if you halt or hesitate in speaking, I will stop writing and your epic will never be written."

"I agree, but you must also fully comprehend the meaning of the poems as you write and not just blindly write them as I say," answered Vyasa.

The elephant headed God gave his consent and they started writing the great epic, *Mahabharata*.

You have already read about Ganesha breaking off his tusk to hurl it at the moon, but other legends claim that he broke his tusk for using it as a pen to write Ved Vyasa's verses.

Ved Vyasa began his narration and Ganesha wrote it down fast. In fact, he was so fast that he did not give Ved Vyasa enough time to even catch his breath!

Ganesha un-mindful of this, went on writing at super speed. Poor Ved Vyasa began to go blue in the face, but Ganesha scribbled on rapidly.

"I will die, if I do not take a break and catch my breath," thought a panicky Ved Vyasa. "I must think of something."

Ved Vyasa then created a very complicated and tricky stanza for the verses. For a split second, Ganesha was confused and he paused to understand before writing.

"Whoosh!"

In those fractions of time, Ved Vyasa inhaled gulps of air. And so whenever Vyasa needed a break, he would narrate a difficult stanza. Ganesha would stall to understand the verse and Vyasa swiftly gasped in a breath!

Thus, the original *Mahabharata* contains many difficult stanzas placed at intervals throughout the length of the epic.

By writing the verses of the great poem *Mahabharata*, Lord Ganesha became the first stenographer in the world! He had taken down the largest book ever composed, dictated by sage Vyasa.

# Attributes of Ganesha

Nearly every aspect and role of Ganesha has meanings and interpretations by which the wisdom of this great God is conveyed to his devotees. The portrayal of Ganesha as a blend of human and animal parts symbolizes the ideals of perfection and spiritual significance.

The most striking feature of Ganesha is his **elephant head.** The large elephant head of Ganesha symbolizes **wisdom** and **understanding**.

According to the legend, the head of a boy was removed and replaced by an elephant's head, symbolic of auspiciousness, strength and intellectual prowess. All the qualities of the elephant are contained in the form of *Ganapati*.

The elephant is the largest and strongest of animals of the forest. Yet he is gentle and, amazingly, a vegetarian, so that he does not kill to eat. He is very affectionate and loyal to his keeper and is greatly swayed if love and kindness are extended to him. Ganesha, though a powerful deity, is similarly loving and forgiving and moved by the affection of his devotees.

The elephant can destroy a whole forest and is a one-man army when provoked. Ganesha is similarly most powerful and can be ruthless when containing evil.

Ganesha's **huge body** is symbolic of the Cosmos or the Universe. The Gods and all mankind, all living things and all manifestations of nature are encompassed within it. The large size is indicative of the role he plays as one within whom the whole universe is contained. Ganesha in the form of *Vishwaroopa* where his body covers the whole universe shows the importance of this deity who is the universe itself.

The **huge paunch** and his voracious appetite (as read in the story *Ganapati & the God of Wealth* -page 36) symbolically shows that God is never appeased or pleased by wealth.

The huge belly also signifies that Ganesha swallows the sorrows of the Universe and protects the world.

The awkward and plump body of Ganesha is symbolic of God's lesson to us that beauty of the outward form has no connection with inner beauty and spiritual perfection.

**Ganesha' trunk** has great significance too. An elephant trunk is strong yet gentle too. This means that you need strength to face the rigours of the outside world, yet you also need gentleness to handle your inner self.

If you notice Ganesha's trunk, it is coiled like an 'OM'. OM is the first word or sound that erupted at the beginning of the world and it is supposed to hold in its single word, veneration to all Hindu Gods and Goddesses.

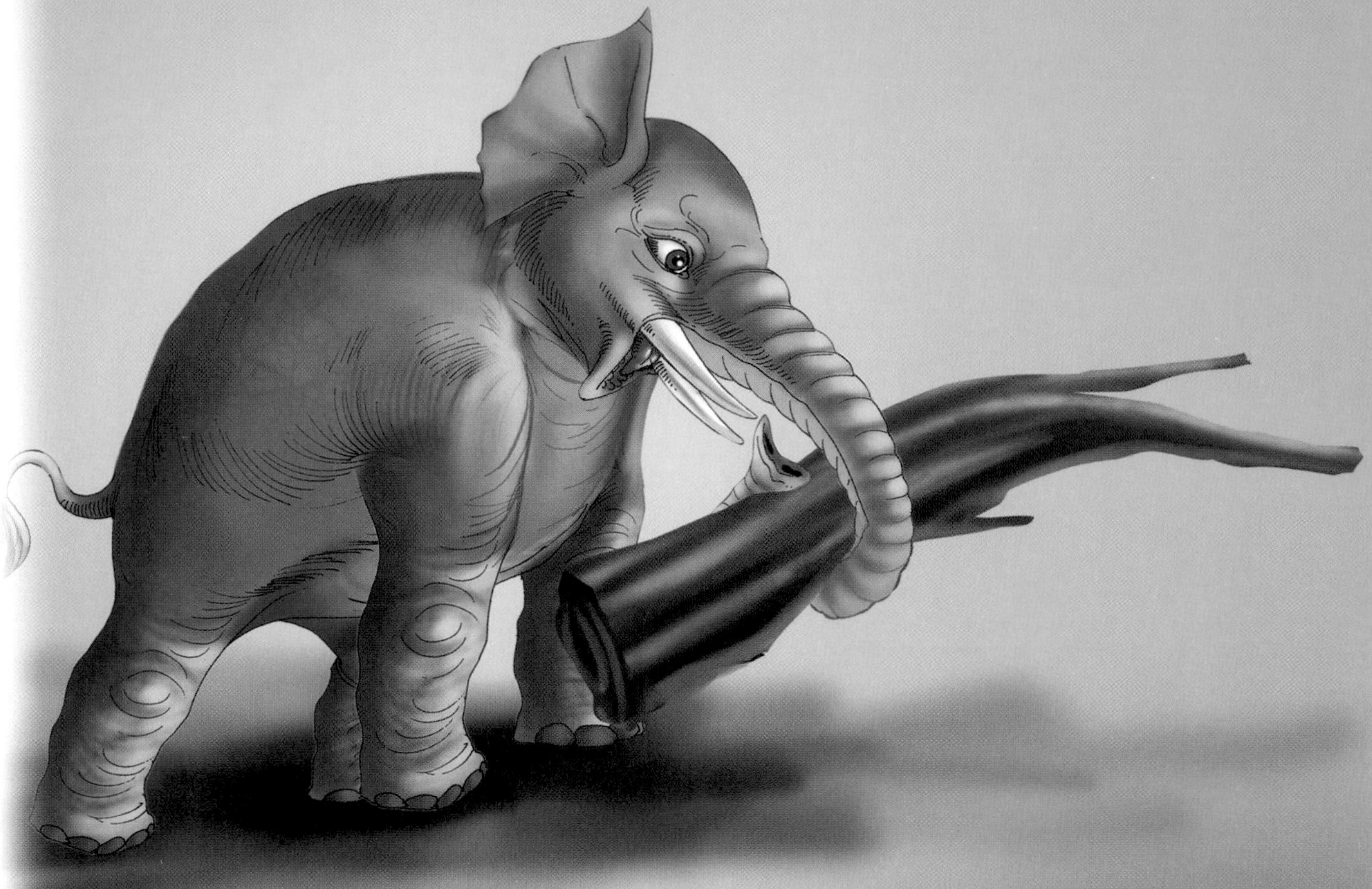

Ganesha's trunk is indicative of his supreme power of discrimination. The elephant uses its trunk to push down a massive tree, carry huge logs to the river and for other heavy tasks. The same huge trunk is used to pick up a few blades of grass, to break a small coconut, remove the hard nut and eat the soft kernel inside. The biggest and minutest of tasks come within the range of this trunk which is symbolic of Ganesha's intellect and its powers of discrimination.

Ganesha sometimes **wears the third day crescent moon** on his head. Symbolically this crescent without blemishes leads human beings to attain pure knowledge and spiritual enlightenment.

Ganesha's **four arms** indicate the aura of a being who is omnipresent.

Ganesha's **elephant eyes** sees things larger than they really are. Thus encouraging the message of respect towards your fellow beings. How is that? When one sees others to be bigger than oneself, automatically, one feels humbled and respect follows naturally.

Ganesha is sometimes shown with **three eyes.** The two front eyes symbolise the power of *Surya* (the sun) and *Chandra* (the moon). The **third eye** is believed to be symbolic of *Agni*, the powerful God of fire. It is located at the seat of wisdom, the centre of the forehead.

The **snake** worn around Ganesha's stomach symbolizes cosmic energy. It is sometimes worn by him as a sacred thread across his left shoulder.

The **large ears** of Ganesha signify great listening powers. To be able to listen to everything without distraction means that one can carefully collect ideas and reach perfection in all ventures.

Ganesha's large ears, like the winnow, sift the bad from the good and the essential truths are conveyed to his worshippers.

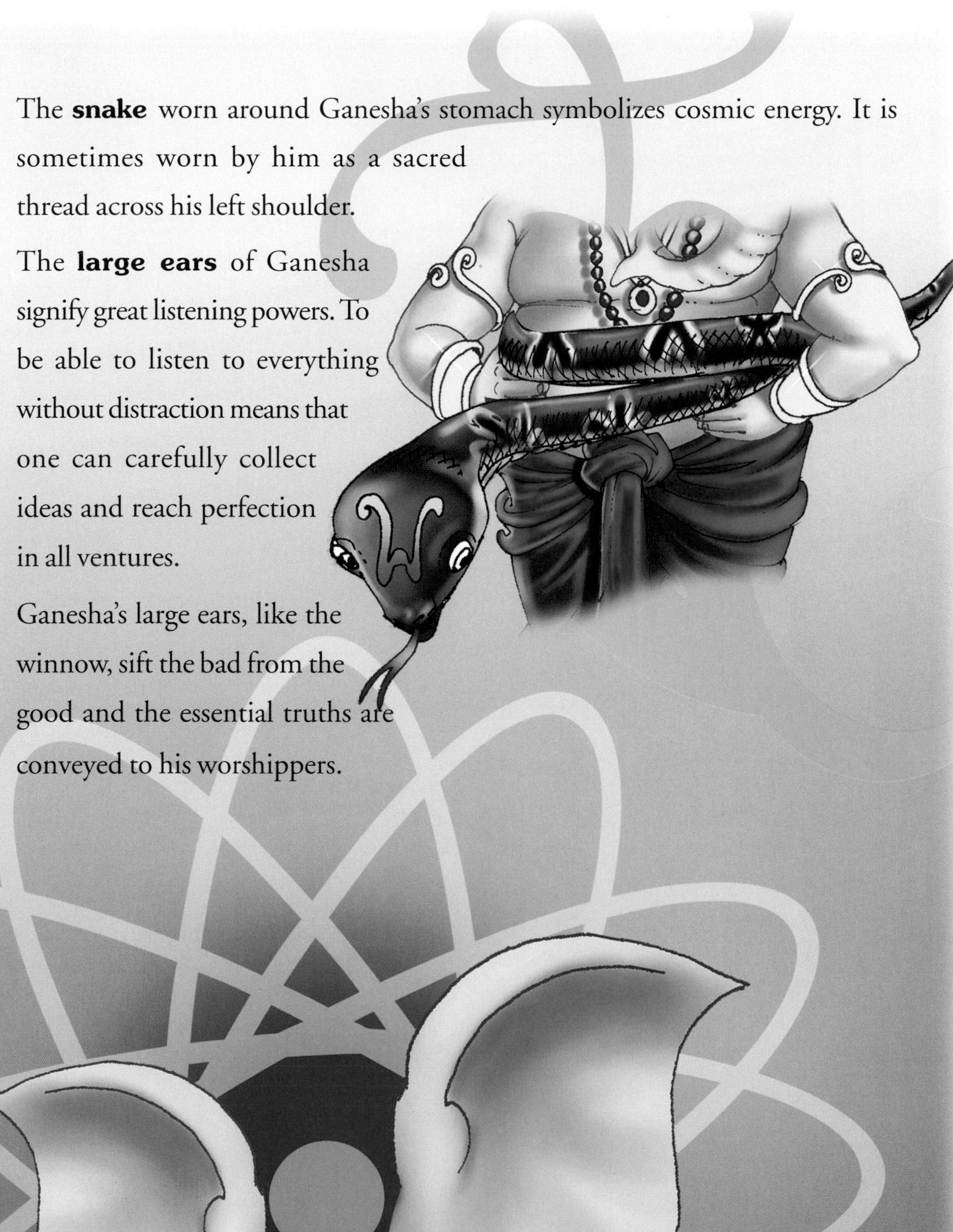

Ganesha has **two tusks** which indicate emotion and wisdom. The broken tusk which goes against all canons of orderliness, balance and symmetry, which are part of Hindu thought, is an unusual facet of Ganesha. Many legends give a reason for the broken left tusk. It is claimed that Ganesha broke the tusk in a war with a demon and another legend says that it was to write the *Mahabharata*.

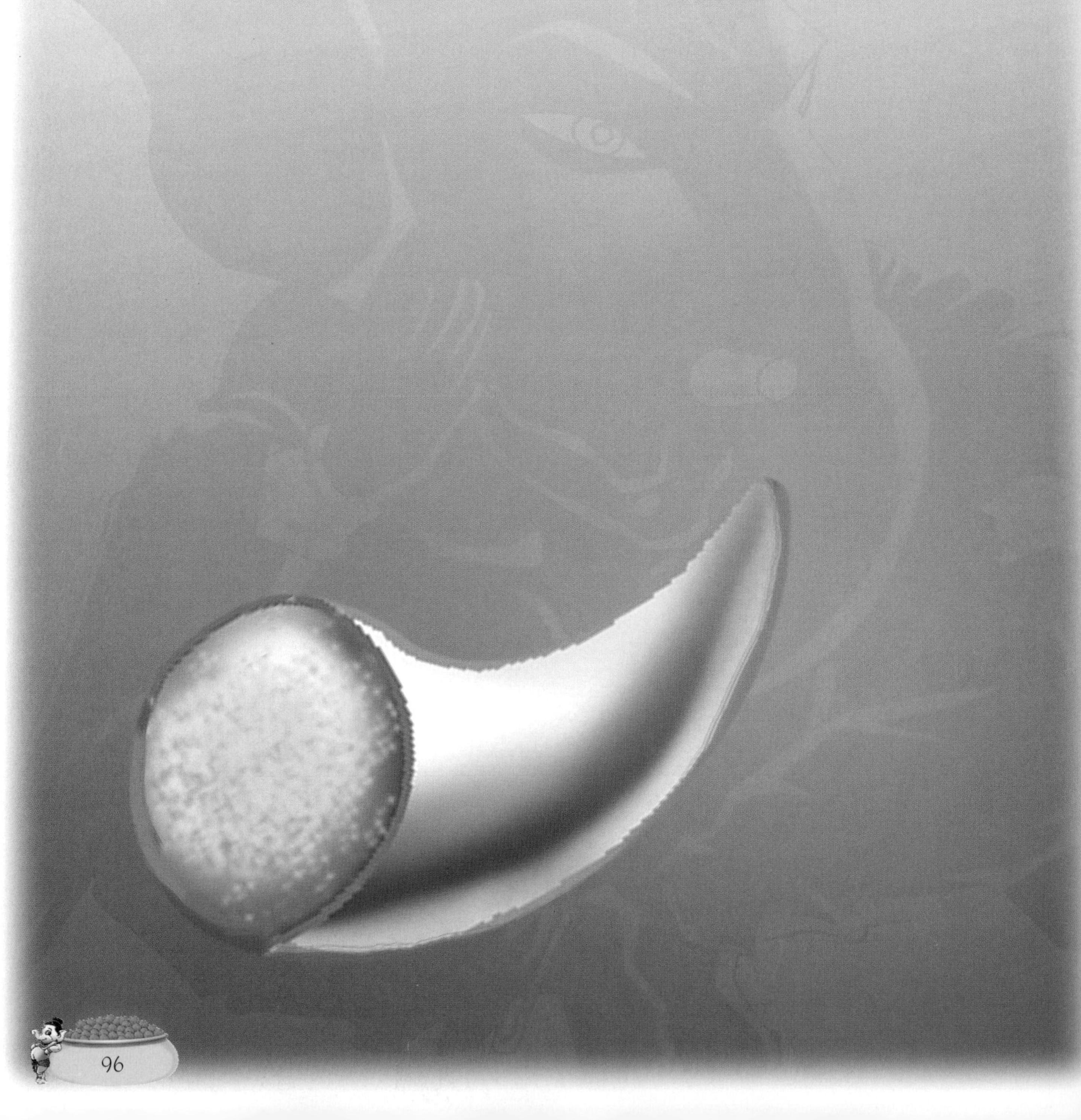

Symbolically Ganesha breaking his tusk to fight with a demon or to write the *Mahabharata* signifies the great sacrifice which Divine Beings make for aiding mankind. It also shows that Ganesha is beyond the rules of Cosmic orderliness as he is the Cosmos itself.

Ganapati is considered a *Brahmachari* (celibate) in most parts of the country. In some areas, *Siddhi* and *Riddhi* are his symbolic consorts. Siddhi represents success and prosperity and Riddhi represents wisdom.

A tray of **laddoos** (sweets) near the Lord denotes that he bestows wealth and prosperity upon his devotees.

Ganesha rides a **mouse.** The mouse symbolises the petty desires of men which nibble away at their personalities and their inner selves. A mouse is compared to ego. An ego, like a mouse, nibbles humility and goodness from human beings. A mouse sitting near the feet of Ganesha indicates that a faultless person is the one who has conquered his or her ego.

Ganesha is shown with other attributes depending on the roles taken by him in his various *avatars.* For destroying demons of evil, he may hold two or more of several weapons. Some of the common ones are a trident, spear, knife, bow, arrow, discus, sword, shield, hammer, mace, snake, Shakti weapon (double trident), large axe, pickaxe, battleaxe, baton, conch, dagger, and stick.

Other attributes seen in his hands in more peaceful roles are a banner, prayer vessel, pot of nectar, pot of gems, prayer beads, flower garland, fly-whisk, *veena,* fruits of various kinds, a sprig of grain, a bunch of flowers, the lotus, a radish, a book, a branch of the wish-fulfilling *kalpavriksha* tree and others.

(The *veena is* symbolic of Nada-Brahmam, the music and rhythm of the Cosmos. The lotus is a symbol of purity as it grows in muddy waters but is untouched by the dirt from which it emerges).

# Some Other Names for Lord Ganesha

| S.no | Name | Meaning |
|---|---|---|
| 1. | Akhurath | One who has a Mouse as his Charioteer |
| 2. | Alampata | Ever Eternal Lord |
| 3. | Amit | Incomparable Lord |
| 4. | Anantachidrupamayam | Infinite and Consciousness Personified |
| 5. | Avaneesh | Lord of the whole World |
| 6. | Avighna | Remover of Obstacles |
| 7. | Balaganapati | Beloved and Lovable Child |
| 8. | Bhalchandra | Moon-Crested Lord |

| | | |
|---|---|---|
| 9. | Bheema | Huge and Gigantic |
| 10. | Bhupati | Lord of the Gods |
| 11. | Bhuvanpati | God of the Gods |
| 12. | Buddhinath | God of Wisdom |
| 13. | Buddhipriya | Knowledge Bestower |
| 14. | Buddhividhata | God of Knowledge |
| 15. | Chaturbhuj | One who has Four Arms |
| 16. | Devadeva | Lord of All Lords |
| 17. | Devantakanashakarin | Destroyer of Evils and Asuras |
| 18. | Devavrata | One who accepts all Penances |
| 19. | Devendrashika | Protector of All Gods |
| 20. | Dharmik | One who is Religious |
| 21. | Dhoomravarna | Smoke-Hued Lord |

| | | |
|---|---|---|
| 22. | Durja | Invincible Lord |
| 23. | Dvaimatura | One who has two Mothers |
| 24. | Ekaakshara | He of the Single Syllable |
| 25. | Ekadanta | Single-Tusked Lord |
| 26. | Ekadrishta | Single-Tusked Lord |
| 27. | Eshanputra | Lord Shiva's Son |
| 28. | Gadadhara | One who has the Mace as his Weapon |
| 29. | Gajakarna | One who has eyes like an elephant |

| | | |
|---|---|---|
| 30. | Gajanana | Elephant-Faced Lord |
| 31. | Gajananeti | Elephant-Faced Lord |
| 32. | Gajavakra | One who has a Trunk of an Elephant |
| 33. | Gajavaktra | One who has a Mouth like an Elephant |
| 34. | Ganadhakshya | Lord of all *Ganas* or Shiva's assistants |
| 35. | Ganadhyakshina | Leader of all the Celestial Bodies |
| 36. | Ganapati | Lord of all Ganas |
| 37. | Gaurisuta | The Son of Gauri (Parvati) |
| 38. | Gunina | One who is the Master of All Virtues |
| 39. | Haridra | One who is Golden Colored |
| 40. | Heramba | Mother's beloved son |
| 41. | Kapila | Yellowish-Brown coloured |
| 42. | Kaveesha | Master of Poets |
| 43. | Kriti | Lord of Music |
| 44. | Kripalu | Merciful Lord |
| 45. | Krishapingaksha | Yellowish-Brown Eyed |

| | | |
|---|---|---|
| 46. | Kshamakaram | Place of Forgiveness |
| 47. | Kshipra | One who is easy to appease |
| 48. | Lambakarna | Large-Eared Lord |
| 49. | Lambodara | The Huge Bellied Lord |
| 50. | Mahabala | Enormously Strong Lord |
| 51. | Mahaganapati | Omnipotent and Supreme Lord |
| 52. | Maheshwaram | Lord of the Universe |
| 53. | Mangalamurti | All Auspicious Lord |
| 54. | Manomay | Winner of Hearts |
| 55. | Mrityuanjaya | Conqueror of Death |
| 56. | Mundakarama | Abode of Happiness |
| 57. | Muktidaya | Bestower of Eternal Bliss |
| 58. | Musikvahana | One who has a Mouse as Charioteer |
| 59. | Nadaprathishta | One who Appreciates and Loves Music |
| 60. | Namasthetu | Vanquisher of All Evils, Vices and Sins |

| | | |
|---|---|---|
| 61. | Nandana | Lord Shiva's Son |
| 62. | Nideeshwaram | Giver of Wealth and Treasures |
| 63. | Omkara | One who has the Form of OM |
| 64. | Pitambara | One who has Yellow-Coloured Body |
| 65. | Pramoda | Lord of All Abodes |
| 66. | Prathameshwara | First Among All |
| 67. | Purush | The Omnipotent Personality |
| 68. | Rakta | One who has a Red-Coloured Body |
| 69. | Rudrapriya | Beloved of Lord Shiva |
| 70. | Sarvadevatman | Acceptor of All Celestial offerings |
| 71. | Sarvasiddhanta | Lord of Principles |
| 72. | Sarvatman | Protector of the Universe |
| 73. | Hambhavi | The Son of Parvati |
| 74. | Shashivarnam | One who has a Moon like Complexion |

| | | |
|---|---|---|
| 75. | Shoorpakarna | Large-Eared Lord |
| 76. | Shuban | All Auspicious Lord |
| 77. | Shubhagunakanan | One who is the Master of All Virtues |
| 78. | Shweta | One who is as Pure as the White Colour |
| 79. | Siddhidhata | Bestower of Success and Accomplishments |
| 80. | Siddhipriya | Bestower of Wishes and Boons |
| 81. | Siddhivinayaka | Bestower of Success |
| 82. | Skandapurvaja | Elder Brother of Skanda (Lord Kartekeya) |
| 83. | Sumukha | Auspicious Face |
| 84. | Sureshwaram | Lord of All Lords |
| 85. | Swaroop | Lover of Beauty |

| | | |
|---|---|---|
| 86. | Tarun | Ageless |
| 87. | Uddanda | Nemesis of Evils and Vices |
| 88. | Umaputra | The Son of Goddess Uma (Parvati) |
| 89. | Vakratunda | Curved Trunk Lord |
| 90. | Varaganapati | Bestower of Boons |
| 91. | Varaprada | Granter of Wishes and Boons |
| 92. | Varadavinayaka | Bestower of Success |
| 93. | Veeraganapati | Heroic Lord |
| 94. | Vidyavaridhi | God of Wisdom |
| 95. | Vighnahara | Remover of Obstacles |
| 96. | Vignaharta | Demolisher of Obstacles |
| 97. | Vighnaraja | Lord of all Hindrances |
| 98. | Vighnarajendra | Lord of all Obstacles |
| 99. | Vighnavinashanaya | Destroyer of All Obstacles and Impediments |
| 100. | Vigneshwara | Lord of all Obstacles |
| 101. | Vikat | Huge and Gigantic |
| 102. | Vinayaka | Lord of All |
| 103. | Vishwamukha | Master of the Universe |
| 104. | Vishwaraja | King of the World |
| 105. | Yagnakaya | Acceptor of all Sacred and Sacrificial Offerings |
| 106. | Yashaskaram | Bestower of Fame and Fortune |
| 107. | Yashvasin | Beloved and Ever Popular Lord |
| 108. | Yogadhipa | The Lord of Meditation |

## God of Auspiciousness...
## The Beginning of all Beginnings

Ganesha, in one way, is the most complex of all Gods. Except as an incarnation on earth, neither God nor His forms as the Trinity or their consorts are ever 'born'.

God only exists.

Ganesha, alone of the deities, was mind-born or created and acquired as a son by Shiva and Parvati.

Yet, amazingly, he is also the simplest, as he is the God of all people, big and small, educated and illiterate. For him, no formalized form of worship is necessary. Meditating on him results in filling one's heart with love of one's fellow beings, human and animal, which is after all the aim of true religion.

This God of wisdom teaches that the path to success and achievement is through the use of the intellect and wisdom.

The calm and majestic Ganesha with the strength and power of an elephant is the Lord of all obstacles which keep Man under control, and yet is also the remover of the obstacles which befuddle Man in his endeavours.

He spreads the message of peace and tranquility and his large size therefore evokes great love never fear. In fact, his unusual form gets embedded in the mind of the worshipper.

He is the playful God of the young and the great guru of the old. He is the God of auspiciousness, the beginning of all beginnings, the saviour of all that is good.

# Children Books By 

## Great Stories for Children *Series*

Size: 8" x 11" – Pages: 48 – Hardbound All Colour – Price: Rs. 99/- Each

Great Stories For Children
(Red Book)

Great Stories For Children
(Green Book)

Great Stories For Children
(Purple Book)

Great Stories For Children
(Yellow Book)

Great Stories For Children
(Black Book)

Great Stories For Children
(White Book)

Great Stories For Children
(Orange Book)

Great Stories For Children
(Brown Book)

Each book is a collection of stories from Indian folklore and myths. Every story is beautifully illustrated and accompanied with appropriate morals to impart wisdom to children. This is a series of 10 books - Red, Yellow, Green, Blue, Pink, Purple, Brown, Orange, Black and White. Each colour book has a different set of stories.

Great Stories For Children
(Blue Book)

Great Stories For Children
(Pink Book)

# Children Books By 

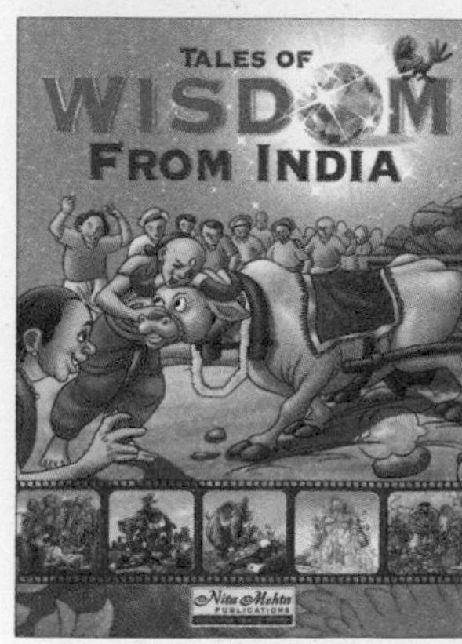

# Children Books By

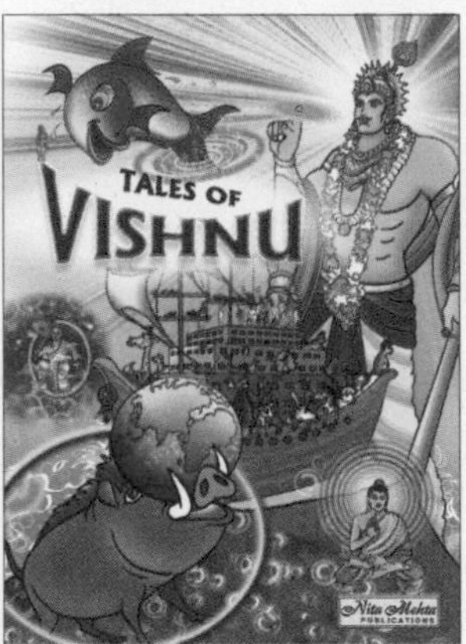

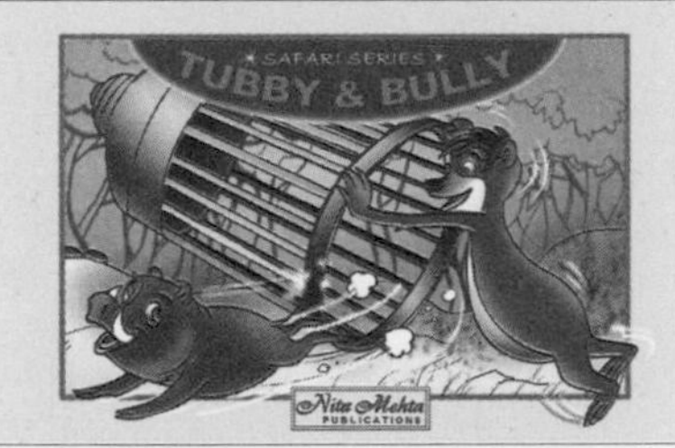